Spreading My Wings

Ron Benson

Lynn Bryan

Kim Newlove

Charolette Player

Liz Stenson

CONSULTANTS

Kathyrn D'Angelo

Susan Elliott-Johns

Diane Lomond

Ken MacInnis

Elizabeth Parchment

Prentice Hall Ginn Canada
Scarborough, Ontario

Contents

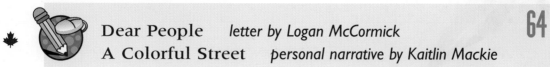

 Selections with this symbol are available on audio.

 This symbol indicates student writing.

🍁 Canadian selections are marked with this symbol.

September Yearning

by Joyce Carol Thomas
Illustrated by Richard Row

Daddy hands me a shirt of many blues
And I've polished my sturdy shoes
And Mama's pressed my overalls
For the very first day of school falls
      in September

I reach for new books
And read about old heroes
I compute numbers
I calculate zeros

Then pages of poems I memorize
And paint the pictures
Behind my eyes

Home Early

by Jackie French Koller

Illustrated by Kasia Charko

Emma and Mrs. March were playing Candyland when a car pulled into the driveway.

"Emma," said Mrs. March, "it looks like your daddy is home early."

Emma jumped up. "Yippee!" she shouted. Emma's daddy had a very important job. He usually came home late. Emma ran to meet him.

"Daddy!" she cried. "You're home early!"

Daddy smiled, but he looked as if he wasn't feeling well.

"Are you sick?" asked Emma.

"No," said Daddy, "just tired." He turned to Mrs. March. "You can go now, thank you, Mrs. March," he said softly. "Emma won't be needing a sitter for a while." Mrs. March nodded and left quietly.

"Why not?" asked Emma.

Daddy looked at Emma, but he didn't seem to see her. "What?" he asked.

"Why won't I need a sitter for a while?"

Daddy's eyes focused again. A tiny smile curled his lips.
"Because Daddy's going to be home for a while."

Emma's eyes widened. "You are?"

Daddy nodded.

"Are you on vacation?" asked Emma.

"Um . . . sort of," said Daddy.

"Yippee!" shouted Emma.

Daddy gave a wheezy little laugh. "Yeah," he said.
"Yippee."

That night at dinner when Mama talked about her job,
Daddy looked out the window.

"Is something wrong?" Mama asked.

"Daddy came home early today," said Emma.

"Early?"

Daddy looked at Mama and Emma. "I lost my job today," he said.

Mama was quiet for a moment, then she reached across the table and squeezed Daddy's hand.

At bedtime Mama came in to kiss Emma good night.

"Mama," she whispered, "will we be poor now?"

Mama smiled. "No," she said, "we'll just be a little more careful about spending money for a while."

"Why is Daddy sad?"

Mama smiled gently. "Daddy thinks we're disappointed in him."

Emma sat up. "No we're not!"

"Of course we're not," said Mama. "But we have to try extra hard to show him that."

"OK," Emma nodded.

When Daddy came in to kiss Emma good night, she threw her arms around him and hugged him extra tight. "I think your boss is a dumbhead," she whispered.

Daddy laughed and kissed her on the nose. "My boss got fired, too."

"Then *his* boss is a dumbhead," said Emma.

Daddy smiled and hugged her. "It's not anyone's fault, Em. But thanks for believing it isn't mine."

"Want to color?" Emma asked Daddy after school the next day.

"Oh, I don't think so, honey."

"I have new crayons." Emma showed him the box. Daddy opened it and sniffed.

"I used to love the smell of new crayons."

Emma held out her coloring book.

"Disneyland," said Daddy. "Can I color Mickey?"

Emma climbed on Daddy's lap and opened the book.

On Wednesday Daddy didn't shave.

"You look messy," said Emma.

"So?" said Daddy. "Who's going to see me?"

"I am."

Daddy went upstairs and shaved.

Thursday Emma took Daddy to the museum. They blew a bubble as big as Emma and made shadow pictures on the wall. Daddy held a baby owl.

"I forgot how much fun museums are," said Daddy.

Daddy took Emma to soccer practice on Friday. Next thing she knew, he was assistant coach.

"I didn't know you could coach soccer," said Emma.

"I'll learn," said Daddy.

Some days Daddy had job interviews. Emma helped him choose just the right tie. When he came home, he was very quiet. Emma was quiet, too. She gave him a big hug, and they made supper together. When Mama came home, she kissed Daddy and squeezed his hand.

Weeks went by, then months, then a year. Emma and Daddy clipped coupons and shopped for bargains. They mended things they used to throw away.

Mostly they had fun together, but sometimes Emma saw Daddy looking out the window, and she knew a worry was growing inside him. Emma stood beside him and held his hand.

One spring day when the air smelled like lilacs, Daddy came home smiling from an interview. He tossed Emma in the air, and she knew the worry was gone. That night Daddy, Mama, and Emma went out for dinner. Emma felt happy inside, but sad, too.

"Why are you so quiet, Emma?" Daddy asked.

"I'll miss you when you go back to work," said Emma.

Daddy reached over and touched her face. "I promise, at least once a month I'll come home early just to be with you."

Emma's eyes opened wide. "But isn't your new job important?"

Daddy smiled. "My new job is important, but I think my other job is a lot *more* important."

"Your other job?" said Emma.

"Yes," said Daddy, "the one I got the day you were born."

Emma hugged Daddy and whispered, "You'll never lose that job."

Collections Galore!

by Lynn Bryan

Why do kids have collections? That depends on who you ask, and what their collections are. How many kinds of collections are there? There are collections galore—that means lots and lots of different kinds. Now meet four kids with four very different collections.

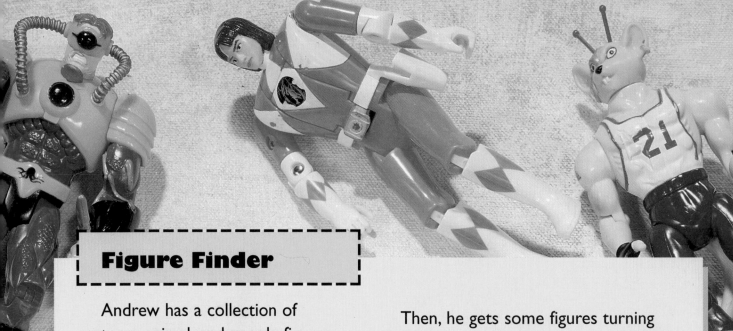

Figure Finder

Andrew has a collection of cartoon, animal, and people figures. It started four years ago when his mom gave him one for a present. Since then, his collection has grown every year.

He has many different sizes and kinds of figures in his collection. "These are my most interesting ones," Andrew says as he takes out some of his action figures.

First, he shows how a few of their heads spin around, and he makes the heads of others pop up on long necks.

Then, he gets some figures turning cartwheels and doing flips. He gives another figure a push and sends it speeding along on roller skates. Andrew winds up the football player's arm and has him throw a ball. Then he takes his rocket man and pulls the cord on the starter blades. The blades begin to whirl around and everything is ready for takeoff. What a show!

Andrew gets figures as gifts and at garage sales, stores, places to eat, and penny carnivals. Who knows how many he will end up with?

Penny Pincher

Kaitlin's penny collection is a rather special one. In it she has pennies that her great grandmother, grandpa, mom, and cousin have collected over the years.

It took a lot of work to get these pennies all sorted. Kaitlin explains. "I made piles of the 1990s, 1980s, 1970s, and so on. I picked the best penny from each year and put it into my penny album." Her oldest penny so far is from the 1920s.

Kaitlin also watches for what she calls "family pennies." These are pennies from years when important things happened in her family. She saves pennies with the same dates as when people in her family were born.

She also has ones from years when there were family weddings and other special events.

Some pennies are harder to find than others, but Kaitlin won't give up. She'll just keep on checking every penny that anyone in her family gets for change at the store. What happens when she gets all the pennies she needs? Maybe she'll start checking their loonies and toonies!

Hedgehog Hoarder

Britney didn't plan on starting a hedgehog collection. It all began when her dad brought home a surprise—a live hedgehog from a pet store!

Britney called the hedgehog Spike. This name suits him, for, as Britney says, "He's kind of prickly all over." Britney wears thick gloves when she picks up Spike. This is partly because of his prickly spines, and partly because he might bite if he gets frightened.

Britney feeds Spike cat food and sometimes a soft banana. Her mom gives him a bath once a year. "Hedgehogs are supposed to like to swim," says Britney, "but Spike keeps trying to get out of the water. I guess a bath isn't as much fun as swimming."

After getting Spike, Britney and her family began collecting hedgehog things. They've found hedgehog books, cards, stuffed toys, figures, candlesticks, and notepaper. Britney even has a hedgehog backpack. Maybe someday she'll use it to take Spike to school for sharing time.

Magnet Minder

Stephanie's collection is kept on her fridge. It's a magnet collection her aunt started her on with a few magnets from the United States.

On a family trip across much of Canada, Stephanie bought magnets along the way. She got ones with photographs or drawings of places of interest, and ones in the shape of the provinces. "When I get all the provinces, they'll fit together to make a map of Canada, just like my magnet map of the United States," says Stephanie.

Stephanie now collects other kinds of fridge magnets as well. She has one with her mom's name on it, a rock from near the Grand Canyon, ones telling about places to eat, and lots more.

The great thing about Stephanie's magnet collection is that it's useful. She can use the magnets to hold up notes and to display her work from school. Her family can order pizza by calling the number on one of the pizza-place magnets. The ones from trips remind Stephanie of different places.

Lots of magnets, lots of uses. There's always a new magnet popping up in Stephanie's collection.

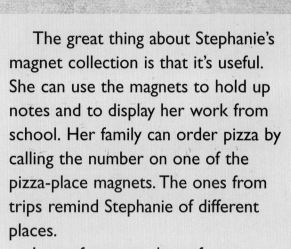

Our Home Is the Sea

by Riki Levinson
Illustrated by Dennis Luzak

Our home is the sea, grandfather said to my father, and father said to me.

I am the eldest son, just like my father. When he was a boy, he did not go to school. I wish I didn't have to. I could be with my father all the time.

Soon he will come for me, for today is my last day of school.

I stuff my report card into a pocket. I do not want mother to see it. She will say that I will be a schoolteacher someday. That is not what I want to be.

I stand on the hill near my school. I can see the sea. My sea.

Down, down the hill I run, to take the tram home.

I get on the tram quickly, run up the stairs, and sit down to watch.

The tram moves slowly. I cannot wait.

We ride through market streets. People crowd around the carts.

A mother with a baby strapped on her back bends up and down, up and down. The baby sleeps.

A man walks through the street carrying two birds. They make loud noises. I do not think they like to be carried by their necks.

At the end of the street, the tram stops. The light is red.

A school bus crosses to the other side of the road.

Little children hop off the bus. Amahs are waiting to take them home.

I cannot wait for the light to turn green.

The tram turns slowly onto a wide street, past tall houses with windows full of plants and drying clothes. I would not want to live in a tall house.

I watch for the park.

When the tram stops, I hurry down the stairs and get off.

I run into the park.

I see an old man standing straight and still under a ginkgo tree. Slowly he lifts his arms and sweeps them around, and stands still again. He looks like a bird.

As quietly as I can, I walk past the old man.

I see the birdmen come and hang their cages on a low berry tree. The men sit down to talk. I think the birds talk to each other too.

I see the peacocks. One comes near and stares at me. I stare back. The peacock lifts its head and spreads its feathers wide. I spread my arms. I wish I had feathers like the peacock.

At the end of the park, I run up the long steps and
cross over the harbor road. I can see our house on the
water. I wave. Middle brother and little brother
wave back as I run down the steps to the wharf.

I put my schoolbag down, take off my shoes, and
wait for mother to come. She poles our sampan to
the water's edge. I step down into our little boat to
go home.

When we get there, I put my schoolbag away. I
will not need it for a long time.

Middle brother and little brother and I sit down
on the floor. Mother fills our bowls with congee and
pours the tea.

The night mist falls gently down as we eat.

I go to bed early. I cannot wait for tomorrow. My
father will come, back from the sea.

Early in the morning, I hear my mother and father talking. I get out of bed quickly and go to him. He puts his hand on my shoulder. I am glad he is near me.

After we eat, we climb down into our sampan and ride out, past the jetty, to grandfather's big boat.

Father and I climb up the ladder.

Mother calls and tells him I will be a schoolteacher someday.

I look at my father. He looks at me. We do not say a word.

I will be a fisherman, like my father and grandfather. Our home is the sea.

ABOUT THE
AUTHOR   RIKI LEVINSON

Riki Levinson was born in Brooklyn, New York. She went to art school, then started her own design studio. She has worked designing both the covers and the insides of books. Since retiring, Riki has written several children's books. She now lives in New York City.

My Collections

Some people like to have collections as a hobby. I collect marbles, rocks, tools, stuffed animals, hockey cards, and pogs. I also have a hat collection with my brother. I got my first stuffed animal from my aunt when I was two. When I was seven, I won a stuffed duck at Klondike Days. In my marble collection I have from peewee to normal to grandfather to King Kong sizes. I have all kinds of rocks in my rock collection. I have one rock that is black and has a white stripe all around it, a shiny crystal, and a rock that looks like a cliff. I also have a piece of petrified wood in the collection. I've picked all these up while I've been on walks. Collecting things is a good hobby for people to have because it gives you something to do in your spare time.

Ben Folarin
Age 9

Ben Folarin

I do most of my writing at school. When I bring my writing home, I talk to my mom about it and she gives me ideas. I like to write adventures best.

I Am Growing Up

My name is Fatimah and I am nine years old. I live with my parents and my little sister. My number one hobby is reading. I read at least one book a day. I also like to write letters to family and friends and make my own cards for them. I am interested in nature and I am curious about how everything works around us. I also have my own garden. I love to act and pretend to be a dancer. I help my mom with some chores, and I enjoy reading to my little sister and playing with her.

Fatimah Nasser
Age 9

Brothers and Sisters

Written and photographed by Ellen B. Senisi

What is it like to have a new brother or sister? Tori is going to find out soon. Her mother is going to have a baby. "Is it going to be a boy or a girl?" Tori

wonders. "Will Mommy love me as much when the baby comes?"

Ben has a newborn brother, and Dorrie has a new sister. Sometimes having a baby in the family is fun.

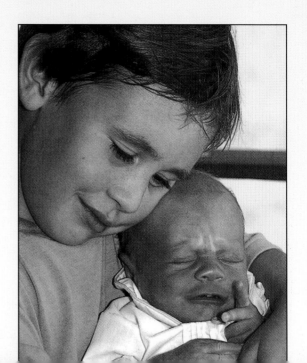

22

"Our new baby is so soft and tiny that I want to cuddle her all the time," says Dorrie.

But sometimes a baby is not so much fun.

"Babies can't do anything by themselves," says Ben. "Mommy still loves me. But she is so busy taking care of the baby, I have to play by myself until he takes another nap."

"I'm so tired of hearing everyone say how cute the baby is," says Valerie.

"I like to hold my baby sister all by myself," says Michael. So does Leo.

Jasmine and Juanita have baby sisters who have learned how to walk. "She's old enough to get into trouble now," says Jasmine, "lots of trouble."

"I help distract my sister," says Juanita. "My mom says I'm the best helper with the baby."

"My sister always wants to do what I'm doing, but she doesn't play games the way you're supposed to," says Alicia.

"Sometimes," says Judson, "we have so much fun together."

Rena is older than her sister. "I know things my little sister doesn't," says Rena. "Now that

she is in kindergarten, I can help her get ready in the morning. And I can take her to her classroom."

"You learn to share when you have a sister," Tori says.

"It's hardest to share our parents," says Rena.

Katelyn and Jordan are almost the same age. So are Ben and Suzannah.

"Sometimes, we're best friends," says Jordan.

"And sometimes we're worst enemies," says Katelyn.

Jeremy and Jonathan are twins. "We have each other to play with all the time," says Jeremy.

Ian and Ryan are twins, too. "Dad says that we even sleep the same way," says Ryan.

"We like looking so much alike that we can trick people."

"We aren't exactly alike, though," says Ian. "I'm better at drawing, but my brother is better at sports."

Sometimes it's hard to be a younger brother.

"It's not fair!" says Peter. "Just because she's older, my sister can do everything better."

And sometimes it's great to be a younger brother.

"She's my other mom," says Steven.

"We have our own secrets," says Tyler. "And we have our own special games."

Trey's older brother and Jesse's older sister are both in middle school.

"He gets mad at me a lot because he thinks I'm a pest," says Trey.

"We get mad at each other a lot," says Jesse. "But then we forget about it."

"Sometimes, my sister is the only person who understands how I feel," says Juanita.

Alex has a teenage brother, and Bianca has a teenage sister. "When can I go everywhere and do everything, just like her?" Bianca wonders.

"Sometimes my sister acts like a grown-up, and we don't have anything to talk about," says Maura. "Other times she's just like me."

"I was adopted," says Sujathi. "Jessica and I came from different moms and dads. But we're still sisters—forever."

Laura and Emma were also adopted. "I tell everybody right away, 'This is my sister!'"

"My dad told me that when they were kids, he and my uncle got into fights. But they still liked each other the best," says Will. "They're grown-ups now and they help each other a lot. They let me help, too."

"My mom said she and her sister used to play school all the time. Now it's for real because they're both teachers," says Eddie. "My mom says her sister is more important to her than ever."

"My grandma and my great-aunt have been sisters for seventy years," says Katherine. "Grandma says her sister is *still* her best friend."

ABOUT THE
AUTHOR ELLEN B. SENISI

Ellen B. Senisi is a photographer and a writer. She has written and taken photographs for four children's books of her own. She has also written and taken pictures for many other magazines and books. Ellen lives in New York with her husband and three children.

Roses for Gita

by Rachna Gilmore
Illustrated by Alice Priestley

Gita tied another small bell on the wire. Done.
She shook the wind chimes and the bells
tinkled. Gita laughed. They didn't sound like
her grandmother Naniji's singing, but they would still
make music for the garden. Gita would hang them on the
fence right above where the First Rose would be planted.

She always thought of it with capital letters—the First Rose, for their new garden for their new home. It had to be a climbing rose, of course—Naniji's favorite.

Right now, the yard was just boring grass, except in the wild overgrown corner where the fence was broken between their yard and mean old Mr. Flinch's. But soon, soon it would be bursting with color, with twisty paths, surprise corners—just like Naniji's garden in India.

Gita put away the leftover bells in the package Naniji had sent, and ran to the dining room.

"Will we get the First Rose today, Mommy?" Gita looked anxiously at the papers scattered on the table.

Mommy rubbed her face. "I have to finish this, Gita. We'll go tomorrow, okay?"

Ever since Mommy went back to university everything was "tomorrow". Everything but her work.

Gita wandered outside to the deep, wide hole she'd dug for the First Rose. Naniji said roses needed space so the roots could grow strong. But what good was the widest hole without a rose bush?

Gita climbed on the picnic table and cautiously looked over the fence. Good—no sign of Mr. Flinch. She straightened up slowly to get a glimpse of his rose-covered archway. How did that crazy old man have such a lovely garden?

She peered through her eyelashes until the flowers blended into streams of color. It was early morning in Naniji's garden. She and Naniji were wandering together, snipping dead blooms, cutting fresh flowers, pulling weeds. The sky was purpley-pink, cool, like Naniji's humming. She always hummed in the garden, sometimes high, sometimes low, like the wind. Flowers grew better, she said, if you sang to them. Gita's throat tightened. Could she hear Naniji humming?

She heard a low rumbling. A bee? Gita opened her eyes. Mr. Flinch, mumbling to himself, shuffled around the corner. Before she could move he growled, "Boy, get down off there. Stop bothering me."

Gita jumped down, heart hammering. Mean old man with his ugly squinty eyes. Always calling her boy, snapping at her.

Once Gita had wandered into his garden and he'd shouted, "Boy, how many times do I have to tell you? Out, I say, out."

Gita stuck out her tongue at the fence. You had to be really nasty to mind anyone just *looking* at your garden. Naniji was always showing people around hers, giving away flowers. They grew better, she said, when they were shared. Mr. Flinch's flowers should all be dead.

Gita woke at sunrise the next morning. She could almost hear Naniji strolling through the garden, singing. Gita dressed and ran outside. A cool breeze murmured over the fence. What was that sound? Music?

Gita squirmed through the shrubs in the corner of her yard. She crept towards the rose arbor and peered through the roses. Someone was playing the violin. Soft and sweet,

swaying with the music. It was Mr. Flinch—his face gentle, glowing with delight.

The roses blurred into soft splashes. Gita wiped her face against her sleeve and tiptoed away.

In her room, Gita shook the wind chimes. When they stopped singing she put them in a bag with a note:

> *Mr. Flinch,*
> *These are wind chimes I made. You can hang them in*
> *your garden for the roses. My name is Gita. I'm not a boy.*
> *I'm a girl. I moved in next door three months ago.*

Before she could change her mind, she ran outside and put the bag in Mr. Flinch's mailbox.

Back in her own yard, Gita stared at the empty hole waiting for the First Rose. She swallowed the lump in her throat. Naniji's garden was kilometres and kilometres away. She flopped down and buried her face in her knees.

She wasn't sure how long she'd sat there when she heard a soft tinkling. She was imagining things. There were no flowers, no singing, nothing.

"Ahem!"

Gita lifted her head.

Mr. Flinch, holding the wind chimes, peered over the fence. The glasses he wore made his eyes big and blurry. Monster eyes.

Gita's heart thumped.

"Well, now, you're a girl all right." Mr. Flinch's voice was creaky and surprised, not shouting or muttering. "Don't those boys live here anymore?"

Gita shook her head.

"Well! I never knew. Can't see much without my glasses. Those boys were always tearing through my flower beds, and . . . I didn't know they'd gone." The monster eyes stared at her. "You, er, Gita, then? Did you give me this?"

"Yes. Naniji, my grandmother, says flowers grow better with music, so . . ." Gita's voice trailed away.

Mr. Flinch's wrinkled mouth widened into a smile. "Well, now, your Naniji is right." He scratched his chin. "Seeing as how you made this, er, suppose you come over and help me hang it?"

Slowly, Gita stood up. She waved through the kitchen window to Mommy, who nodded her head.

Gita eased through the shrubbed corner and followed the winding path to the rose arbor.

"Now then," said Mr. Flinch, "where shall we hang this?"

Gita took a deep breath and stared at the flower beds filled with shades of blue, yellow, red.

"There!" She pointed to a nail sticking out from the centre of the arbor.

Mr. Flinch reached for a ladder leaning against the shed. His thin arms shook slightly.

"Let me do that," cried Gita. She clambered up the ladder and hung the wind chimes.

"Thank you," Mr. Flinch smiled. He reached up and shook her hand.

"You're welcome," said Gita, softly. The skin on the back of his hand was loose and crepey, bulging with veins—just like Naniji's.

"Now then, I've got something for you," said Mr. Flinch. He cut a bunch of roses, trimming the thorns. "You come over again, now, eh?" he said, handing Gita the bouquet.

Gita stared at him for a moment. Mr. Flinch didn't have monster eyes at all. They were soft and blue, like forget-me-nots.

"I will," Gita said. "Oh, Mr. Flinch, we're getting the First Rose for our garden today. I want one like this." Gita pointed to the rose arbor. "What kind is it?"

"It's an Explorer rose," said Mr. Flinch. "Grows great around here." He sniffed and rubbed his head. "Mind you, now, Gita, you've got to start it right—dig the hole big and wide."

"That's what Naniji says," cried Gita. "Oh, Mr. Flinch, would you come over and help me plant it?"

A sudden breeze hummed past Gita and set the wind chimes ringing. Mr. Flinch's face lit up as it had when he'd played the violin.

He cleared his throat. "Well, now, if you'd like, I'll do that."

Gita smiled. She'd make new wind chimes and the First Rose would dig its roots down, down towards Naniji's garden on the other side of the world. It would stretch its branches strong and high—maybe even dance over the fence to Mr. Flinch's violin.

two friends

by Nikki Giovanni
Illustrated by Marisol Sarazin

lydia and shirley have
two pierced ears and
two bare ones
five pigtails
two pairs of sneakers
two berets
two smiles
one necklace
one bracelet
lots of stripes and
one good friendship

Ivan and the All-Stars

by Kathleen Cook Waldron
Illustrated by Anne Villeneuve

Ivan's family moved again—this time to a little house on the West Side. Mom was busy unpacking boxes. "This is our last move," she promised, "you'll see. You'll like it here. You'll make new friends."

Ivan crawled into an empty box. "No, I don't see," he said. "I don't like it here, and I won't make new friends."

"You won't make new friends? Why not?"

"I'm going to be a star. Rich and famous. I won't have time for friends."

"A star! That's wonderful! But don't you want friends too?"

"No," Ivan replied firmly. He had already made up his mind. Making new friends was hard. Being a star had to be easier. "I want to be a star," Ivan said, "and I will be a star. You'll see."

I think I'll be a movie star, Ivan decided after the first week of school. From watching television he knew that if he wanted to be a movie star, he would have to go to Hollywood.

But how? he wondered. It's too far to walk. Airplanes, trains, and buses cost too much. I don't think Mom will drive me. What can I do?

Then Ivan had an idea.

I'll go downtown to CCTV. They'll know what to do.

"I want to go to Hollywood and be a star," he told the lady at the front desk.

"Don't we all," the lady replied, popping a peppermint into her mouth.

"I want to be a star," Ivan repeated. "Can you help me?"

"Honey, if I knew how to be a Hollywood star, would I be sitting here?"

Ivan started to answer, but the lady didn't hear him. The phone rang and she turned away. Ivan looked around the room. Hollywood *is* far away, he thought. Maybe too far.

I think I'll be a rock star, Ivan decided after school the next day. A movie star has to move. But a rock star can star in his own garage.

Ivan chased the spiders out of the garage, swept up the cobwebs and dust, and made his broom into a guitar. He painted a sign and sold tickets for five cents each.

The twins across the street, Jamie and Jessie, bought two tickets. Meredith, the girl next door, brought her cat, Stretch, but she only bought one ticket because Stretch sat in her lap.

Ivan sang and danced and threw his guitar around. Everyone cheered when the show was over. Stretch purred.

"Way to go, Ivan-O!" Jamie shouted.

But Ivan's rock show was a lot of work for fifteen cents, three people, and a cat. To become a rich and famous rock star, Ivan would have to spend a lot more time in the garage.

So Ivan decided to be a baseball star. He had a ball and glove. Movie stars had to move. Rock stars had to spend too much time inside. But a baseball star could play outside *and* be home for dinner.

Ivan took his ball and glove to the park. Jessie, Jamie, Meredith, and two boys from Ivan's class were playing a game of scrub. Stretch lay curled up on a blanket a safe distance from home plate.

"Yo, Ivan!" Jamie called. "Take left field."

"Sure!" Ivan called back. *Now* I'll be a star, he thought.

But Ivan had never played baseball. He'd played a little catch, but he'd never actually *played baseball*.

Balls dropped to Ivan's right. They fell to his left. In front of him. Behind him. One ball dropped on his head.

When it was his turn to pitch, balls flew everywhere. Ivan had an arm like a pea-shooter gone wild.

Batting was even worse.

Ivan swung too soon.

He swung too late.

He swung at pitches inside, outside, high, and low.

Once he almost hit Jamie with his bat.

But he never hit the ball.

When the game was over Ivan stood alone out in left field. It was getting dark. A cold wind tugged at his shirt. He kicked the dirt with the toe of his shoe and slowly started walking home.

I'll never be a star, thought Ivan sadly, scuffing up dust clouds with every step.

The next day after school, Jamie and Jessie ran up to Ivan.

"Coming to play baseball?" Jamie asked.

"I don't think so . . ." Ivan said quietly.

"Why not? We need you," Jessie said.

"We'll meet you there!" Jamie yelled.

Ivan rushed home to get his ball and glove and ran to the park. He and Jamie and Jessie took turns pitching and hitting and catching.

Stretch arrived and settled into his position, followed by Meredith, Ravi, Kacie, and Chico from Ivan's class.

They played together until it was too dark.

Ivan played baseball every day, and every day he played a little better. In fact, Ivan was so busy playing baseball that he almost forgot about being a star. Almost.

"We have enough players now for a regular team," Jessie said after Jake and Haley joined them. "But first we need a name."

"How about the Wildcats?" Meredith suggested.

"Or the Blazing Bats?" said Jamie.

"Or . . . the All-Stars?" said Ivan. "The *West Side* All-Stars?"

"Yes!" everyone agreed. "The West Side All-Stars!"

At last Ivan was a star.

At Saturday's game he ran back, back, back to deep left field and caught his first fly ball.

Billy's World

by Cora Weber-Pillwax
Illustrated by Matt Gould

The boy stood on a hill overlooking a lake.
Snowflakes were falling.
Some ravens flew by.
He saw skidoos far out on the lake.
Uncle James was ice-fishing with two friends.
Billy loved winter.
There was no doubt about that.
But winter could get lonely.
Billy had gone back to school in September.
He had many friends there.

But there were times when something just seemed to be missing.

The boy turned away from the lake.

He had only one day left of school.

Then it would be the weekend.

He saw Jeannie and Pat coming down the road.

Billy ran on down the snowy hill to catch up.

The children laughed and scuffled on their way to school.

After school Billy stopped to watch his Dad at work.

Dad was helping to build the new community centre.

Billy waved to his Dad and ran on home.

Mom had left a note on the fridge door.

Dear Billy,
I've gone to get groceries. Cindy is baby-sitting at Auntie's.
Joey is with me. I'll buy some chocolate ice cream for dessert.
Love, Mom

Billy put the note in his pocket and closed the door behind him as he left.

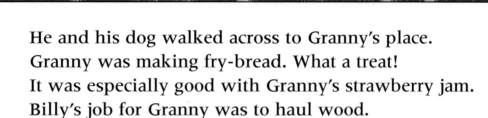

He and his dog walked across to Granny's place.

Granny was making fry-bread. What a treat!

It was especially good with Granny's strawberry jam.

Billy's job for Granny was to haul wood.

This was an important job because Granny loved her old wood stove.

Mom's electric stove didn't need wood!

At the wood pile, a weasel popped his head out at Billy.

And there it was again—that same feeling!

Something was missing.

Friday afternoon, Billy and Grampa loaded the skidoo into the truck.

They were going to the trapline.

They needed many things for the weekend.

They packed the guns, snare wire, lantern fuel, and radio batteries.

They also packed bedrolls, an axe, a shovel, a power saw, and some rope.

Granny had packed food for them.

On the way to the cabin, the boy watched the snow falling lightly from the branches of the trees.

He saw deer and moose tracks in the ditches along the road.

Grampa showed him where a wolf had crossed the road about an hour earlier.

Grampa stopped the truck beside the cabin.

Billy jumped out.

Two squirrels scurried up the old spruce tree.

The squirrels chattered as Grampa and Billy unloaded the truck.

Suddenly Billy heard the "whoosh-whoosh" of wings as a great owl flew off.

Then he understood what he had been missing.

It was the peace and loneliness of the bush.

And yet, this loneliness throbbed with life.

The great owl had pulled him in to share in that circle of life.

Inside the cabin, Grampa lit the gas lamp. Then he helped Billy build a fire in the stove.

After supper, Billy listened to Grampa tell stories.

Then Billy went to bed. He listened to the crackling fire. Far away a wolf, or maybe a coyote, was howling.

Billy felt warm and safe.

This was home to him, too.

He wondered how his friends at school would feel if they were here.

He fell asleep dreaming of owls talking to children, and wolves racing by his side through heavy snowdrifts.

ABOUT THE AUTHOR CORA WEBER-PILLWAX

Cora Weber-Pillwax was raised at Calling Lake, Alberta. She has two children and six grandchildren. She says that she "loves to write. It is an activity of peace . . . writing allows me to live anywhere. I can live in a cabin in the bush and still be able to write and 'talk' to people."

Responsibilities

In my family I have responsibilities like taking out the garbage and making my bed. Sometimes I take care of my brother. Most of the time, I don't like to take out the garbage but I still do it. Everyone in my family has some responsibilities but my mom and dad have the most. I would like to learn to make spaghetti sauce.

Michael Rowley
Grade 3

When I write I think of fiction stories and things that are true. I put them into a web and then I make a story.

Michael Rowley

My Family

My family is fun and so are you.
We skip and play with friends like you.

We show our love with kisses and hugs.
We camp outside with squirrels and bugs.

My house is nice, my sister is too.
We always say, "I love you."

Samantha Pickles
Age 7

I like writing stories about me and I like to read books.

Samantha Pickles

The Day They Saved Her Majesty

by John Brown and Rick Book
Illustrated by Joanne Fitzgerald

Laker was five years old when her father first took her to the forest just outside Mapletown. They walked along a path that wound through the shady woods, went down into a ravine, and circled around a large pond. There were fish and beaver in the pond, and deer and racoons and rabbits in the woods. Most of the trees were maple trees. The biggest maple stood in the middle of the forest. Laker and her Dad stood under it, their heads tilted way back. They could hardly see the top.

"This tree is probably a hundred years old," said Laker's Dad.

"It's so tall and beautiful—like a queen," said Laker. "I think we should call it Her Majesty."

Ever since that day, Her Majesty was like a home in the woods for Laker and her friends. On hot summer days, she and her best pal, Jimmy, and Jimmy's big brother, Mikey, played hide-and-seek in the trees around Her Majesty. They sat in the shade against her trunk and told stories. They made brightly painted birdhouses and hung them from Her Majesty's branches. Way up high, hidden in the leaves, they built a tree house. Sometimes, they brought picnics and climbed the rope ladder into the tree house and pretended they were shipwrecked sailors. Laker even had her eighth birthday party up there.

Then one day, the mayor of the town called a meeting. He told everyone the forest outside Mapletown had been sold. The town had to clear the land so the new owner could build a shopping mall. Everyone was surprised and very sad except the mayor, who said the town needed the money.

"Besides," the mayor said, "that's progress."

Laker's Mom and Dad told her the news. Laker thought of Her Majesty. She thought of the other trees, too. And of all the birds and animals who would lose their homes when the forest was cut down.

"They can't do that!" she said. Then she started to cry because she knew they could.

That Saturday, Laker, Jimmy, Mikey, and their friends gathered at the tree house one last time. They had made their favorite sandwiches and brought their favorite drinks. But no one felt like eating.

No one felt like playing, either. They just sat there and talked quietly.

"I saw a beaver at the pond this morning," said Jimmy.

"I saw a Great Blue Heron," said a friend.

"Where will they go when the forest is gone?" asked Mikey.

"Where will we play?" asked another.

"I wish we could do something to stop them," said Laker with a sigh.

"They won't listen to us," Mikey said. "We're just kids."

Soon the terrible day came. A truckload of workers arrived. They started their chain saws; they swung their axes. Chips of wood flew. Huge trees groaned. One by one, they crashed to the ground. A bulldozer roared as it dug out the stumps. A crane hoisted the logs onto big trucks that rolled away to the sawmill. Hour after hour, the little forest grew smaller.

Laker and Jimmy and their friends came to the woods to watch. There were no bird songs that day. The scream of chain saws, the crash of trees, the roar of the bulldozer filled the air. By noon, the whole town was there. Hundreds of people watched silently. Tears rolled down their cheeks. No one knew how to stop the cutting, Now it was too late.

Finally, all the trees were down except one. Her Majesty stood alone. The old maple towered over a field of stumps and a tangle of broken branches.

"Cut it down!" the mayor ordered. It was Her Majesty's turn.

Suddenly, Laker broke away from the crowd and ran to the tree she loved so much. She tried to climb up the tree-house ladder. But a woman in a white hard hat grabbed her and pulled her back. Laker's father led her to safety.

A worker stepped up, pulled a cord, and started his chain saw. Laker closed her eyes. The worker looked at Laker. He looked at Laker's friends and at all the sad faces of the people gathered around. Suddenly, he reached down, shut off the chain saw, and said quietly, "I can't do this."

"Neither can I," said another worker.

"I'm going home," said another

"You can't quit now," yelled the mayor. He signalled to the bulldozer driver to knock down Her Majesty. With a roar, the bulldozer turned toward the tree.

Suddenly, Jimmy ran past the bulldozer to the base of Her Majesty. "No, no, no, don't do it!" he yelled.

Laker pulled free of her father's hand and ran to Jimmy. The bulldozer kept moving. Then Mikey ran out. Then their friends ran out. Then their moms and dads ran after them. And then—the huge crowd of townspeople rushed toward the children and the tree. They joined hands and made a circle around Her Majesty. They stood there and faced the bulldozer. They watched as it crawled toward them.

"Children should have trees to play in," someone yelled.

"Adults need woods to live by, too," cried an old lady.

"Wildlife need wild places to live," said Laker's Dad.

Suddenly, just a few metres from the people, the bulldozer stopped. The driver looked at the mayor, turned off his engine, and climbed down.

"That's it," he said. "The kids are right."

There was a hush in the crowd. The mayor looked at the people. He was very angry.

"Where's your common sense?" he asked. "I'll get somebody else to cut this tree down." And he walked away in a huff.

The people started talking all at once. They laughed. Some cried. Dogs barked. Laker hugged her Mom and Dad. Everybody shook hands with Jimmy and Laker and told them how brave they were.

A few days later, some of the parents and townspeople went to court. They stopped the mayor from cutting down Her Majesty. One month later, in the town elections, the mayor was defeated. The new mayor promised to plant trees over the whole area. And she did. The townspeople raised the money. They bought two trees for every maple cut down. Everyone came to help plant them.

It took many years for the trees to grow. In fact, Laker and Jimmy grew up, both got married, had children, and then grandchildren before Her Majesty was surrounded by big, beautiful maple trees once again. For all that time, the people of Mapletown have told the story about the two children who saved Her Majesty and of how Jimmy Laker Park got its name.

Hoot Club
Super-Projects

Going Green

Hats off to the Grade 3 class of Morna Heights School in Saint John, New Brunswick. These keen-green kids did forty-three of the one hundred environmental projects that their school completed to become a Green School. Their projects included planting trees along an eroding bank and planting tulips to honor war veterans. Now they're working on more projects to become a Jade School. Go kids go!

Baking Up a Forest

When Matthew Noel realized that hectares of rain forest disappear every day, he wanted to do something to help the animals that live there. He talked to his classmates at Hillcrest School in Nairobi, Kenya, and they decided to hold a cake sale. The kids baked up lots of goodies and raised enough money to preserve several hectares of the animals' rain-forest home.

Ring Around the Birdy

The Grade 3 students at H. G. Olsen School were sick and tired of seeing plastic six-pack rings around the necks of local birds. So to help protect the birds and other animals on their island home, the kids gathered up the rings from every place they could think of. They collected two thousand to three thousand rings and sent them to a company that recycles them. Ring it in!

Keen on Green

Seventy-five kids from Connaught School in Regina, Saskatchewan, have been getting their green thumbs in shape. The kids planned and planted a garden of prairie plants in a corner of their schoolyard. First they learned all they could about the plants. Next they got busy planting seeds. And when the seeds grew into plants, they transplanted them outside. Now not only does their playground look cool, but the kids have created a home fit for local insects. Give these kids a big green thumbs up!

Save the Swamps

Jamie Ross and his fellow Wolf Cubs in Toronto, Ontario, grew bulrushes and planted them in nearby wetlands to give local animals a place to call home!

Club Adopts Meanie

Who: Teddy Harrison, Tristan Thompson, and classmates

Where: Vancouver, British Columbia

Project: Teddy and Tristan got some of their classmates together and formed a club to help the environment.

What They Did: The Club members pooled their pocket money together and bought a gift certificate for books. Then they sold raffle tickets for the gift certificate. They also held sidewalk juice sales. When the club had collected just over $100.00, they decided to help marmots survive in the wild by using the money to "adopt" a marmot named Meanie in his natural home.

What They Learned: "Trying to make things happen takes patience."

Message to Other Kids: "Knowing what you did is fun in the end."

Allison's Enviro Challenge

After you read a letter, what do you do with the envelope? Throw it out? Think again! Last year, Allison Altdoerffer, 8, reused the same envelope over and over again, carrying monthly book orders to and from school for a whole year. And she challenged her classmates to do the same.

Tender Loving Earth Care

The kids at Georgetown Elementary School in Prince Edward Island celebrate Earth Day all year long! They're an incredible conservation crew. They cleaned up a beaver dam and pond close to their school.

The Georgetown crew also created their own nature trail. First the kids removed heaps of junk from a nearby stream.

Then they planted trees, built bridges and nesting boxes, stocked the pond with fish, and built an access trail. Next, they put up signs to identify the trees and habitats. They even planted wild rice to help attract ducks and geese. And this awesome amount of work was just the beginning. The Georgetown environmental crusade continues! The kids have cleaned up an old garbage dump and planted trees at their school. Keep up the good work!

Cedar-y Clean!

Lots of exhaust fumes and noise from passing-by traffic was invading the yard of Rosedale School. So the students looked for and found a neat pollution solution. They planted a cedar hedge along the edge of the schoolyard near the road. The cedars help to reduce the noise and clean the air—cedar-y clean.

The Catfish Palace

by Hazel J. Hutchins
Illustrated by Ruth Ohi

The pet store near Cindy's house had been called The Catfish Palace for as long as anyone could remember. The cages were clean, the water was fresh, and the young budgies chattered happily on their perches. There were also plenty of small aquarium fish, but the catfish for which the store was named was not small. He was large and flat and round and sat at the bottom of his tank all day. Day after day. The tank had been built especially for him with tall cement walls, but it was not really large enough for a fish his size.

Some of the customers who looked in the tank laughed when they saw such a large fish sitting on the bottom.

Some of the customers who looked in his tank became very interested and asked how old he was and where he was from and if he had a name.

Some of the customers who looked in his tank said nothing and went on to look at other things. Cindy was one of those people.

"I feel sorry for the big catfish at the pet store," Cindy told her mother one night. "Why is he there?"

"I think he's their mascot," said her mother. "Perhaps he started out small and then got large and there he is. I know his tank isn't very big, but I don't think they could find a bigger aquarium for him even if they tried."

Cindy told her father about the large catfish.

"Yes, I've seen him," said her father. "He makes me sad too, but it's not as bad as things once were. In the old days some storekeepers had wild animals chained up outside their stores—a bear or a wolf on a very short chain—and they were never taken off the chain. I'm glad people aren't allowed to do that anymore. I don't think the catfish is as unhappy as those animals were."

Cindy asked the lady next door about the large catfish.

"I know how it feels to be sad about a fish," said the lady next door. "When I was a child in the old country my mother used to buy a live fish at the market and bring it home and put it in our bath tub. Just when I began to feel friendly towards it, we'd eat it for supper."

Cindy knew that they were all trying to make her feel better, but she still felt sorry for the big catfish.

One day Cindy heard a veterinarian talking on the radio. He had studied a sea mammal called a dugong. He explained that tears fall from the eyes of the dugong. Some people believe the tears are valuable. In one place where the veterinarian had lived, a person with a house near the ocean had captured a dugong. The person had treated it unkindly, hoping to make it cry more, and then the person had collected its tears.

"And . . . and did he keep it for a long time?" asked the interviewer.

"I suppose he might have," said the veterinarian quietly. "But one morning I got up very early, before anyone else in the village was awake, and released it back into the ocean."

It made Cindy feel good to hear the man tell, so simply, how he had helped the dugong.

For many nights after that Cindy dreamed of doors and locks and waves rolling up a beach. But she could not do what the veterinarian had done. She could not open locked doors. And the catfish was so many kilometres from any place it might be able to call home.

Cindy stopped going to The Catfish Palace. All summer, when she needed something for her own pets, she went to another store, even though it meant a long bike ride across town. In November, however, snow fell deeply and Cindy's bike was put in the shed. Once again she had to return to The Catfish Palace.

It was the same as always— dark and warm and heavy with animal smells, but clean enough and with a feeling that the animals were well cared for. Cindy would have had good feelings about it except for the cement tank along the wall. Then she noticed someone was cleaning out the tank. In fact, when she walked right up to it, she realized the tank was empty.

"What happened to the big catfish?" asked Cindy.

"He was very old," said the girl who was scouring the side. "He died a few days ago."

"Are they going to get another one?" asked Cindy.

"I think so," said the girl. "After all, the name of the store is The Catfish Palace."

That night Cindy wrote a letter to the owner of The Catfish Palace. She told him about how the big catfish had made her feel. She told him about the old days when bears and wolves were kept on chains in front of a store. She told him how instead of making her want to go into the store, the big catfish had made her not want to go inside. She told him she could understand how people could take something for a pet by mistake, not really understanding how big it might get, but she asked him not to buy another big catfish. She said perhaps he could change the name of his store instead.

Cindy did not receive a reply to her letter.

All winter, whenever she walked by the store, she looked to see if the name on the sign had changed, but it had not.

But one day when she and her mother were walking by, Cindy did see a change. The big round cement tank now stood against the front window. Someone had built cardboard castle turrets above it. Someone had strung colored Christmas lights over it. Cindy felt a soft, sad lump in the pit of her stomach. If anything, this was worse than before.

"Cindy, let's just pop in and see what they've got in that big tank," said her mother.

Cindy shook her head.

"I don't want to," she said quietly .

"I don't know," said her mother. "They don't usually put tanks with fish in them right up against the glass like that. It's too hard to keep the temperature at the right level."

So Cindy and her mother went into the store. Her mother looked first. Cindy saw a smile spread across her face. In fact, her mother actually giggled.

Then Cindy peeked over the edge. There was a green lawn, some miniature patio furniture and trees. Spread on the lawn and in the furniture and on the trees were all kinds of toy cats. Each had his or her fishing hook dangling into a little tub that was marked "donations— S.P.C.A."

One of the cats had a little heart pinned to her hat. It read "For Cindy."

Now sometimes Cindy still thinks of the big old catfish. Sometimes she still thinks of bears chained up by country stores and the story of the dugong. She knows there are many other things she will see that may make her sad. She knows the world is not perfect, and she will not always do the perfect thing herself.

But she also knows it is never too late to try and do things better.

And she often takes her friends to see the cats fish at The Catfish Palace.

ABOUT THE AUTHOR   HAZEL J. HUTCHINS

Hazel J. Hutchins grew up on a farm in southern Alberta, where her mother read to the children every day and her father recited poetry. As a young girl Hazel loved books and dreamed of becoming a writer. Now, her books are published in Canada, the United States, and Great Britain.

Dear People

Dear People,

I feel sorry for endangered animals. Do you? How would we feel if our homes were being cut down or if we were being hunted? That's no fun for the animals. In the rain forest, many trees are being cut down and precious animals are dying. The animals that survive are homeless. I wish people would just stop! We need trees that are alive, not dead. Some trees that are being cut down are even ending up as toothpicks.

I think that if Mother Nature got trees this far, we should leave them alone. What do you think?

Your friend,
Logan

Logan McCormick
Grade 3

I like writing because I can create characters and I also like to take people to new worlds.

Logan McCormick

Usually I get my ideas from what I do. I write lots of letters to my best friend and tell her what I'm doing. We started that in kindergarten when our moms would write something we said and we'd copy it.

Kaitlin Mackie

A Colorful Street

Do you know why I planted flowers in my Grandma's garden with her? Well, I did it because I wanted to make the street look colorful. We have to water the plants so they won't die. I use a watering can so I don't waste water. I pull the weeds too and take dead flowers off the plants. If we don't look after the flowers the street will look ugly.

Kaitlin Mackie
Grade 3